Diarrhea, Diarrhea:
And other poems for children

a collection of poems by Sigmund A. Boloz

illustrated by Antoinette C. Boloz

Autumn C. Boloz, editor

© 1998 Sigmund A. Boloz (text)

© 1998 Antoinette C. Boloz (art)

ISBN - 1 - 886635 - 15 - 3

cover illustration by
Antoinette C. Boloz, age 11, colored pencil

Dedicated with love to my family.

I hear that it can be hard living with a writer. Writers have curious habits. They often write during strange hours and their messy work spaces have to be just so. When an idea grabs them, they can become focused and isolated; they can be lost to the world. They are forever writing and when they are done writing, they find ways to write some more.

Writers' desks are trash heaps of glorious ideas and treasures which are littered with notes written on post its, scraps of paper, bubble gum wrappers, the backs of envelopes and odd-sized receipts, napkins and in the margins of other notes. Why, I even remember once dragging in an old, wooden 2 x 4 because I couldn't find a piece of paper and I had written a poem on it.

For putting up with this writer, I dedicate this book to my family.

To my best friend, my wife Irene, thanks for driving me to young authors' visits and conferences while I wrote some more and thanks for those wonderful cups of hot chocolate without which I could not write.

To my daughters, Angelita, Autumn and Antoinette, always remember that you are special people. You have inspired so many poems through our happiest and saddest times.

To my son, Stoney, follow your dreams they are important because they matter to you.

To my grandchildren, Nichelle and Jacob, thanks for being yourselves and for inspiring my weirdest poems. Your poems make children laugh the hardest.

I also want to give a special thanks to the children of John F. Long School in Phoenix, West Sedona Elementary, South Beaver School, Fort Wingate Elementary and to the other schools where we continue to write. Your ideas began several of these poems and gave me the courage to keep writing for children.

With love, Sigmund A. Boloz,
Ganado, Arizona, July 1998

Table of Contents

THE SWEETEST TASTE

Strawberries and bananas
On a flashlight night,
Glow incredibly,
So vivid and bright.

Like twinkling stars
They dance and play
And then as if swallowed
They fade away.

Only to be topped by a row of cherries,
A string of pearls,
Flashing and crackling
Each booms and twirls.

And young children
With their picnic blankets spread,
Lick their lips in anticipation,
Then cover their ears and heads.

For there is nothing more delicious
Than watching ice cream sundaes fly,
Nothing but the sweet taste of freedom . . .
On the Fourth of July.

Sigmund A. Boloz

HEAVIER THAN MY BRAIN

The ideas do not pour forward,
No matter my stare,
My pen lies rigid, cold,
Rather lifeless there.

A heartbeat is nonexistent.
This situation is quite bizarre.
I give it mouth-to-mouth,
Try to revive it with CPR.

There is still no movement.
So, I tap it repeatedly, hard,
All the time wishing this class
Had stationed a certified lifeguard.

But still the ideas do not pour forward,
No matter my stare,
My pen lies rigid, cold,
Rather lifeless there.

So, I struggle within the moment,
Sharing its obvious pain.
Oh, how I wish for an inspiration when my pen
Is heavier than my brain.

Sigmund A. Boloz

THE JUMP

There he rushed,
Speeding down the hill.
Faster and faster.
I see him still.

Pedaling and pumping,
Toward the show.
Eyes fixed on the jump.
Bent really low.

Shirt tail flapping.
Hat pulled down tight.
Bracing for the moment.
Launched into flight.

And there in that instant,
Up into the air,
Rider descending to the left,
Bike tumbling there.

Everyone gasps!
Soft dust begins to clear,
Checking for arms and head,
A loose finger or ear.

But as luck would have it,
Everything was still there,
One ego bruised
Under disheveled hair.

Slightly damaged.
But nothing a smile could not hide.
No worse the wear.
A case of lightly dented pride.

Sigmund A. Boloz

3

MAMA WENT TO TOWN

(a march)

My dear mama went to town,
In and out and up and down,
In and out of every store,
In and out of every door.

One, two, three, four,
One two . . . three four.

She bought caps and coats galore.
She kept buying more and more.

One, two, three, four,
One two . . . three four.

My dear mama went to town,
In and out and up and down,
In and out of every store,
In and out of every door.

One, two, three, four,
One two . . . three four.

She bought pants and tops galore.
She kept buying more and more.

One, two, three, four,
One two . . . three four.

My dear mama went to town,
In and out and up and down,
In and out of every store,
In and out of every door.

One, two, three, four,
One two . . . three four.

She bought shoes and socks galore.
She kept buying more and more.

One, two, three, four,
One two . . . three four.

My dear mama went to town,
In and out and up and down,
And I think that she's still there,
Buying lots of underwear.

One, two, three, four,
One two . . . three four.

Sigmund A. Boloz

GOT UP IN THE MORNING

(a poem for two voices)

Got up in the morning,	
	peaceful, peaceful morning,
Crawled up out of bed,	
	messy, messy bed,
Washed my sleepy face,	
	tired, tired face,
Combed my bushy head,	
	sleepy, sleepy head,
Ate a little breakfast,	
	lazy, lazy breakfast,
Walked outside to wait,	
	long, long wait,
Waited for my friend,	
	slow, slow friend,
So, both of us were late,	
	really, really late,
Sent to the office,	
	boring, boring office,
Had to see the man,	
	mad, mad man,
Didn't want some trouble,	
	terrible, terrible trouble,
Had to make a plan,	
	big, big plan,
So, I blamed my little brother,	
	crying, crying brother,
Kept me up all night,	
	restless, restless night,
Didn't get my sleep,	
	restful, restful sleep,
Till the morning light,	
	dizzy, dizzy light,

6

So, I said . . .

Got up in the morning,

peaceful, peaceful morning,

Crawled up out of bed,

messy, messy bed . . .

Sigmund A. Boloz

NOTHING TO EAT

Too many choices,
But noting to eat!

Too dry,
too greasy,
too salty,
too sweet!

"No! Not that!"
"This one won't do!"

Too sticky,
too gooey,
too hard
to chew!

"I never liked that!"
"Oh, what a stink!"

Too gross,
too scummy,
too oily,
too pink!

"This causes indigestion!"
"Too much cholesterol!"

Too slimy,
too brown,
too heavy
to haul!

"I want something creamy!"
"I want chocolate stuff!"

Chocolate-covered candy!
Chocolate covered caramel!
I want chocolate, luscious chocolate
too much is never enough!

Sigmund A. Boloz

8

BELLY BUTTONS

Cover up your belly button.
Don't let it show,
Cause if you do
Then everyone will know,

Know whether yours is an inny or an outy,
It's just not something you'll outgrow,
So cover up your belly buttons
Or everyone will know.

Sigmund A. Boloz

DIARRHEA! DIARRHEA!

(Poem for two voices)

Had to go to the bathroom,

        distant, distant bathroom,

Really really quick,

        fastest, fastest quick,

Stomach was aching,

        swishy, swishy aching,

Was feeling awfully sick,

        really, really sick.

    DIARRHEA! DIARRHEA!

Rolled to the left,

        couldn't, couldn't left,

Rolled to the right,

        couldn't, couldn't right,

Stuck in the covers,

        tangled, tangled covers,

From tossing all night,

        sweaty, sweaty night.

    DIARRHEA! DIARRHEA!

Ripped off the covers,

        tangled, tangled covers,

Fell off the bed,

        high, high bed,

Slammed to the floor,

        wooden, wooden floor,

Hit my aching head,

        dizzy, dizzy head.

    DIARRHEA! DIARRHEA!

Sprinted to the bathroom,
       distant, distant bathroom,

But I had to wait,
       pleading, pleading wait,

Banged on the door,
       closed, closed door,

But it was too late,
       really, really late!

DIARRHEA! DIARRHEA!

Sigmund A. Boloz

NIGHTMARES UNDER MY BED

Five little nightmares under my bed.
Daddy grabbed one and bopped him on his head.
He put him in a sack and this is what he said,
"Why don't you live somewhere else instead?"

Four little nightmares under my bed.
Daddy grabbed one and bopped him on his head.
He put him in a sack and this is what he said,
"Why don't you live somewhere else instead?"

Three little nightmares under my bed.
Daddy grabbed one and bopped him on his head.
He put him in a sack and this is what he said,
"Why don't you live somewhere else instead?"

Two little nightmares under my bed.
Daddy grabbed one and bopped him on his head.
He put him in a sack and this is what he said,
"Why don't you live somewhere else instead?"

One little nightmare under my bed.
Daddy grabbed him and bopped him on his head.
He put him in a sack and this is what he said,
"Why don't you live somewhere else instead?"

No little nightmares under my bed.
Daddy picked up his sack and this is what he said,
"Five little nightmares once lived under your bed,
But I'm taking them over to your friend's house instead."

"NOW, GO TO SLEEP!"

Sigmund A. Boloz

THE CRUD

It's that time of year,
When the crud goes around,
When you will become another statistic
Who the crud has found.

And you can hide if you choose to,
But it doesn't matter much,
Cause you can get the crud from a sneeze
Or from something that you touch.

And while some may argue
If it's a cold or the flu,
While you're feeling lousy,
It won't matter much to you.

For while the crud might grab your stomach,
Or it might even invade your head,
The crud just absolutely ruins
The fun of staying home sick in bed.

So, use those ten thousand tissues.
And don't forget to wash your hands,
But the crud will eventually attack your throat,
Your tonsils and your glands.

So drink plenty of liquid
And take your Vitamin C,
But the crud will eventually . . .
Eve, eve, even get you and me.
Ah, ah, ah, Cho-o-o-o-o!
Sorry . . . Tissue?

Sigmund A. Boloz

13

UGLY VALENTINE
(a song)

I might seem so very ugly,
To someone as cute as you
But if you should ever love me, baby,
I shall forever be true.

So, kissy, kissy, baby!
Smoochy, smoochy, smoo!
But call me, call me baby,
For I do really love you.

Sigmund A. Boloz

FLOWERS
(a poem for two voices)

It's highly overrated.
It's too commercialized.

> But I love it.
> I was hoping you had realized.

It's not really important.
And you know I already care.

> But I love it.
> And I'd love to see one there.

It's environmentally unfriendly.
And the flower only dies.

> But I love it.
> Just look into my eyes.

But it takes too much time.
And it's such a pain.

> But I love it.
> Now, isn't that very plain?

Well, if I have to.
I guess I can.

> Now, that's why I love you.
> You're such a romantic man.

Sigmund A. Boloz

LET'S TALK
(a poem for two voices)

Boys talk about wrestling and greasy food.
        Girls talk about the future and attitude.

Boys talk about cold, mushy stuff and cheese.
        Girls talk about diets and calories.

Boys talk about Mike and cool skateboards.
        Girls talk about shopping and its rewards.

Boys talk about new comics and the latest video games.
        Girls talk about handsome boys and beautiful names.

Boys talk about half-pipes, crashes and scars.
        Girls talk about jealousy and movies stars.

Boys talk about movie monsters and super heros.
        Girls talk about losers and total zeros.

Boys talk about nuclear weapons and mass destruction.
        Girls talk about boys and plan introductions.

        Girls talk about how immature boys can be,
Boys . . . Hey, was she talking about me?

Sigmund A. Boloz

16

GORILLA LOVE

You'll never find a girlfriend.
No nice girl could ever love you.
I mean, you're worse than ugly
You're out-of-shape and hairy, too.

Your mama's a gorilla.
Your sister is, too.
Your best friend's a monkey.
Your dad lives in a zoo.

But you'll never find a girlfriend here,
I think I should already know.
Living inside a cage,
Is just not a smart way to go.

Sigmund A. Boloz

17

VALENTINE'S CANDY: JUST FOR YOU

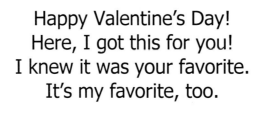

Happy Valentine's Day!
Here, I got this for you!
I knew it was your favorite.
It's my favorite, too.

The wrapper was so clean,
A beautiful, striking hue.
So, I opened the wrapper carefully,
Smelled chocolate and cashew.

The candy had such a wonderful aroma,
My interest grew and grew.
So, I took one small taste for me . . .
And then I took one for you.

The candy was so very delicious,
I took another few.
The candy was so tasty,
So creamy rich to chew.

Well, one thing led to another
And pretty soon I was through,
But I knew you would love this. So, I saved . . .
This nice wrapper just for you.

Happy Valentine's Day!

Sigmund A. Boloz

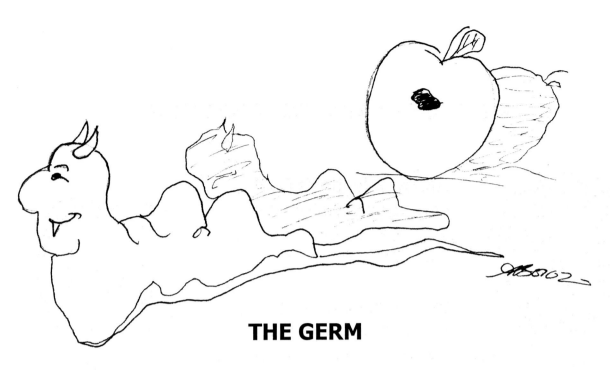

THE GERM

It started in my stomach
In the middle of winter term,
As I sat at my desk
And began to wiggle and squirm.

I was feeling quite strange,
I really must affirm,
That my head felt like an apple
With a burrowing worm.

Then my bones began to ache
As if crushed by a pachyderm,
And my lunch, still within my stomach,
Was feeling less than truly firm.

So, my mom took me to the doctor
And there he did surely confirm,
That I was feeling less than myself
All because of a tiny germ.

Sigmund A. Boloz

PIZZA DIET

I'd like to order
Two pizzas please,
Large, make those extra large,
With extra cheese.

With extra pepperoni,
As much sauce as you can squeeze,
With extra sausage and extra olives,
With a lot of those and these.

Don't scrimp on those mushrooms,
Peppers and salty anchovies,
Cause, when you're balancing the four basic food groups,
Who cares about the calories.

Sigmund A. Boloz

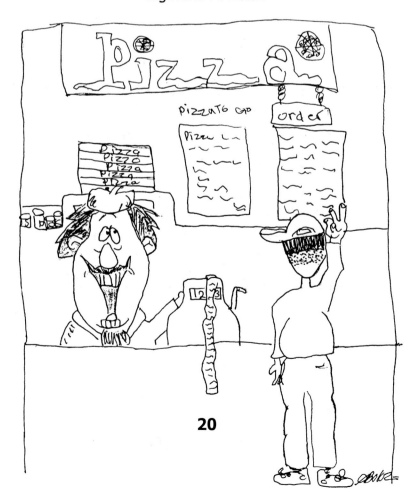

WHAT ARE YOU DIGGING FOR?

What are you digging for,
What do you suppose?
Are you looking for a gummy worm
Up inside that nose?

It's certainly not a place for a three-ring circus
Nor a customized van.
It's no place for a model train set
Nor a ninja from Japan.

But it must be something important,
The way you twist and strain.
What are you digging for,
Are you trying to find your brain?

Sigmund A. Boloz

21

LOST AND FOUND

Dear Teacher,
     I am sorry to report to you
          that I cannot give my book report today,
     For I seem to have lost my voice somewhere,
          but where, I cannot say.

     I just got up this morning and apparently,
          my voice had up and gone,
     Left me sometime last night, I imagine,
          without a syllable of my lexicon.

     And if I will find it sometime this week,
          I also do not know,
     I mean, exactly where does one look for a lost voice,
          I mean, where does a lost voice go?

Thankfully,
Speechless ME

Sigmund A. Boloz

I HATE BUGS!

I washed my hands ten thousand times
But I'm still as worried as could be,
Cause momma says that I might be catching the bug,
She says, "We'll just have to wait and see."

But I don't want to catch a bug!
They are gross and slippery!
Anyway, I didn't think bugs came around
When it's cold and wintery.

Sigmund A. Boloz

23

REVISIT YOUR FAMILY TREE

Why don't you go visit your ancestors,
I'd be glad to drive you to the zoo.
Then maybe we could drop you off
And you could spend a year or two.

I mean, why don't you go back,
Revisit your family tree.
You know, get up into those branches
And act like a real chimpanzee.

Why don't you go bother one of your own kind,
Another hairy little ape.
And maybe this time they'll put you in a larger cage,
So next time, you will not escape.

Sigmund A. Boloz

GIRLS ARE SMART

Girls like to play school.
We love to play with toys.
And we clean up when asked
Unlike those messy boys.

Boys like to lay around.
Boys are extremely lazy.
They like to play with stinky bugs
Which us girls think is crazy.

On the other hand, girls are smart.
We like to play with jacks.
And when boys might try to kiss us
We give them several wacks.

Girls like to stay at home,
Clean up and shake out the rugs,
While we dream of marrying those stupid boys
With their stinky, ugly bugs.

Sigmund A. Boloz

25

BANDAGES

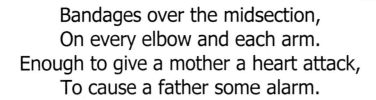

Bandages on ankles.
Bandages on feet.
Bandages covering bandages
Everywhere they meet.

Bandages on kneecaps.
Some on each side.
Bandages where people can see,
Some which I hide.

Bandages over the midsection,
On every elbow and each arm.
Enough to give a mother a heart attack,
To cause a father some alarm.

Bandages covering every square inch
Up to the top of my head,
And with this many bandages
It's a wonder that I'm not dead.

Bandages on my neck and face.
Making it so hard to see.
Next Halloween, I'm not letting my brother
Make a mummy out of me!

Sigmund A. Boloz

LIGHT WEIGHT

Inside your belly button,
In between your toes,
Up inside your ears,
Sometimes up your nose,

Deep inside your pockets
All throughout your hair,
Lining both sides of your socks,
Sand is everywhere.

So, get into that bathtub
And scrub, scrub away in there.
I'm sure you'll only weigh half as much,
When you lose that sand you wear.

Sigmund A. Boloz

FRANK EINSTEIN

Oh, my son, your report card,
It makes your papa so proud,
To think, my son is the one
Who stands up in the crowd!
Yes! Yes! By golly!
There they are!
With grades like these, my son,
You shall go **F**ar!
There's a **F**abulous in mathematics!
And a **F**irst-rate in spelling, too!
Fantastic! **F**antastic! My son,
Fantastic are you!

You're **F**ar better than your brother,
He only gets **A**'s,
That **A**wful **A**lbert is so **A**verage,
I think that I shall ground him today.
My **F**irstborn son, my **F**avorite son,
I told you not to read that book!
You've made your **F**ull-blooded papa feel so **F**rabjous,
You are **F**amous my **F**risky little snook!

I heard that your tearful teachers have been calling,
And now I understand why!
Because you're just as **F**ormidable as your **F**orefathers,
You **F**ull-**F**ledged-genius little guy.
The other parents are **F**rankly jealous
Because we are **F**ortunate to be so blessed,
And to think, you're my little **F**rank Einstein,
You're just **F**iner than the rest!
And there's a **F**reethinking in reading!
A **F**rontrunner in language, too!
Fantastic! **F**antastic! My son,
Fantastic are you!

Sigmund A. Boloz

28

VEGETABLES

I love vegetables,
Leaves, roots, bulbs and seeds,
But not because they provide a kid with
All the vitamins a person needs.

I mean, vegetables cooked,
Or vegetables raw,
Are in every bowl of salad or soup
That I ever saw.

But to tell you the truth,
Give my stomach a rest,
For when vegetables roll off my tongue
Is when I like them best.

For instance, I like the way saying broccoli
Makes my mouth wild,
And sometimes I wonder how rutabaga
Got thus compiled.

I like to say zucchini, asparagus,
Rhubarb and artichoke,
And who ever named the eggplant
Came up with a good joke.

I like to say parsley, parsnip, peppers,
Peas, pumpkins, and peanuts really quick,
But when I still think of garlic, horseradish and onions,
They have a way of making me sick.

So I do like vegetables,
Everyone that I never ate . . .
Because I like them best when they roll off my tongue
And when they fall off of my plate.

Sigmund A. Boloz

29

SLAM!

Ever since the time
when I was young
and very small,
about the time
when I learned
that I could crawl,
my mother bought me
a rounded ball
and I began to dream
of being really tall,
Tall enough
to dibble,
to jump,
to fly,
to slam dunk
that basketball.

Sigmund A. Boloz

Other books by Sigmund A. Boloz:

Who Speaks For The Children?
illustrated by Christine F. Hackett
Published by the Arizona Reading Association (1993)

A Wondrous Ride: and other Poems for Children
illustrated by Abraham Jones
Published by Wooded Hill Productions (1994)

Clouds Before The Storm
illustrated by Abraham Jones
Published by Wooded Hill Productions (1994)

Prairie Dog Dreams
illustrated by Abraham Jones
Published by Wooded Hill Productions (1995)

Odious Mud
illustrated by Preston A. Boloz
Published by Wooded Hill Productions (1995)

From Daybooks to Night Logs: Journeying with Journals
Published by Wooded Hill Productions (1996)

The Learning Never Stops
illustrated by Abraham Jones
Published by Wooded Hill Productions (1996)

The Distance Across One's Heart: Poetry for the Writer
illustrated by Abraham Jones
Published by Wooded Hill Productions (1997)

Recess Chaos
illustrated by Abraham Jones
Published by Wooded Hill Productions (1997)

Be Dangerous
illustrated by Antoinette C. Boloz
Published by Wooded Hill Productions (1998)

Posters by Sigmund A. Boloz

Learning (color)   There is a Need... (black and white)

    This is my Right (color)   It Begins in the Hogan (color)

I Loved My Way Into Language (color)   Be Dangerous (color)

            Published by   **WOODED HILL PRODUCTIONS**
                             Post Office Box 825
                             Ganado, Arizona 86505
                             (520) 755-3774

Antoinette C. Boloz, Sigmund A. Boloz and Autumn C. Boloz

Sigmund A. Boloz was born in Melton Mawbray, England and came to America at an early age. He grew up speaking Polish and for a time lived in Hartford, Connecticut before moving to his hometown of Newington, Connecticut. A graduate of the University of Connecticut, he received his advanced degree from Northern Arizona University in Flagstaff. He has been principal of Ganado Primary School since 1980. In 1997 he was named the **National Distinguished Principal from Arizona**.

Ganado Primary School has received numerous awards including national recognition from **NCTE, IRA**, the **U.S. Department of Education**, and the **Native American Scholarship Fund, Inc**. In 1995, Ganado Primary School was named an **A+** school and the **Number One School in Arizona**. In 1997, Ganado Primary School was named a **National Blue Ribbon School of Excellence** by the U.S. Department of Education.

As a poet and writer, Mr. Boloz has produced ten books of poetry and has published pieces and articles in over 70 different journals and books. He is a member of the **Author's** Guild.

Antoinette C. Boloz is a sensitive eleven year old and has been drawing and painting since she was five. Toni's beautiful personality comes through in her art which has appeared in several books now. Currently her interests include oil painting and professional wrestling.

Autumn C. Boloz attends Northern Arizona University in Flagstaff, Arizona. If she ever lost the power to laugh her heart would break. "Auz" is dedicated, focused and is known to be a loyal friend.